Parenting with Patience

Chap Bettis

Author of *The Disciple-Making Parent*

Parenting

with

Patience

Overcoming Anger in Your Home

DIAMOND HILL
PUBLISHING

PARENTING WITH PATIENCE: Overcoming Anger in the Home
Copyright © 2019 by Chap Bettis.
Diamond Hill Publishing
All rights reserved.
ISBN-13: 978-0-9990410-3-1
ISBN-10: 0-9990410-3-7

TABLE OF CONTENTS

About the Author

Chap Bettis is the author of *The Disciple-Making Parent: Raising Your Children to Love and Follow Jesus Christ*. Since its release, *The Disciple-Making Parent* has quickly become the premier resource for helping families and churches pass the gospel to their children. It has been endorsed by a growing list of Christian leaders including: Dr. Al Mohler, Tim Challies, Dr. David Murray, Dr. Tim Lane, Dr. Wayne Mack, Marty Machowski, Jackie Kendall, and David and Sally Michael. More information is available at www.thedisciplemakingparent.com or on his podcast – The Disciple-Making Parent.

Chap is also a frequent conference speaker and the executive director of The Apollos Project, a ministry devoted to helping parents disciple their children. His articles have appeared on the websites of The Gospel Coalition, The Ethics and Religious Liberty Counsel, Rooted, and Crosswalk.

For the previous 25 years, he was lead pastor in a New England church plant. He and his wife Sharon have four adult children and reside in Rhode Island. He also authored *The Donut Date Journal, Evangelism for the Tongue-Tied*, and The *Fearless Apologetics Curriculum*.

When he is not ministering the Word, Chap likes cycling, skiing, reading, and checking out Providence restaurants with his wife. You can follow him on Twitter or Instagram @chapbettis or on his blog at theapollosproject.com.

Introduction and How to Use this Study

Anger is an enormous problem in the Christian home and Christian church. As parents we often struggle in secret with this sin. Or we don't struggle at all. We feel justified in our anger. And after we explode and the kids are scattered, we alternate between feeling guilty and feeling relieved. Rarely do we take time to think about what caused the explosion. We are on to the next event rushing at us.

This study intends to do something about this problem. We want to take a look at what the Bible has to say about the subject of anger. Rather than succumbing to a sin-confess-sin cycle, we are going to learn scriptural and practical strategies to become more patient parents.

It is possible to grow in this area. And we must! Our children are precious to God and us. Our anger destroys something in them. In addition, children are one of God's sanctifying pressures in our lives. As we embrace this pressure, we will emerge more mature and patient.

Overview of Each Lesson

You will notice that this workbook is made up of five lessons. Each lesson consists of two videos to watch, a place to take notes, and discussion questions to answer. Real change happens with others. As we confess sin, ask for prayer, and are encouraged in community, we start to change.

You can find the videos for purchase at www.ApollosU.com.

Each lesson also includes five days for individual Bible study. It is the Word of God that the Spirit uses to change the people of God. Make sure you take time to hear from God in his Word.

An Anger Journal is also included in each lesson. Although we don't cover it thoroughly until Lesson 5, it his helpful to start recording anger incidents as they occur. A key tool of change is the Anger Journal. Although the explanation of the journal is located at the end of the study, feel free to insert that lesson anywhere you think would be helpful. It stands alone. No matter when you study Lesson 5, make use of the journals at the end of each lesson.

Teaching This Study

This study is intended to be a video-driven Bible study. It can be formatted a number of different ways.

A 5-7 Week Small Group Study. Used in this way, you can start with discussing key questions from the previous week's devotional. Then watch one lesson consisting of two videos totaling around 20-25 minutes. Finish with some discussion and a prayer time centered around the video that was just watched.

A 10-13 Week Study. This might be more suitable for those who want a longer and less intense study. It would allow a longer discussion time. You could follow the same format as mentioned above: discuss the previous week's important devotional questions, watch the video together, and then discuss the material you have just seen. In this scenario, the five-day study could be spread out over two weeks.

Individual Study. The material is designed for group study but can be used individually. Online classes will be opened up several times a year.

Writing Out the Scripture

One aspect of this study is a little bit unusual. You will notice that I ask you to write out some of the verses. You may be tempted to skip this portion. Don't! The king of Israel was commanded to write out the Scriptures (see Deuteronomy 17:18). Scientists are continuing to discover how writing ideas on paper seals them in your mind. You will benefit from this small habit.

Intended Audience

This study is targeted for followers of Jesus Christ – those who have repented of their sins and trusted in his full atonement on the cross. However, if that is not you for some reason, you will still be helped by the teaching in this material. Several times we will think explicitly about the gospel and the call to profess genuine faith in Jesus Christ alone. Please think seriously about Jesus' call to repent and believe the gospel.

Further Reading

For further reading on anger you might consider Dr. David Powlison's *Good and Angry: Redeeming Anger, Irritation, Complaining, and Bitterness*; Dr. Ed Welch, *A Small Book about a Big Problem*; and Dr. Robert D. Jones, *Uprooting Anger: Biblical Help for a Common Problem*. All of those resources have their unique strengths and will help you in the fight.

For further reading on parenting, my own *Parenting with Confidence* material will be available soon. In addition, I commend *Shepherding a Child's Heart* by Tedd Tripp and *Don't Make Me Count to Three* by Ginger Plowman Hubbard.

Finally, I would love to connect with you. Comment on our social media pages and tell me how the Lord has used this material in your life. Sign up for our weekly email at theapollosproject.com website. Every Friday I send out thoughts and suggested articles about parenting.

I am praying the Lord's blessing on your study. If you are ready, then let's get started.

Chap Bettis

LESSON
1

Introduction and Three Foundational Issues

LECTURE NOTES

LESSON 1

Video A: Introduction

A Survey of Where We Are

1. Anger permeates the _____.

2. Anger is often _____ in the church.

Why?

    It is a hidden sin.

    We are not always _____ it is sin.

    We don't realize how large our reactions are and how they impact others.

    We don't understand the _____ of anger.

    We are embarrassed.

A Survey of Where We are Going

3. An overview of our lessons.

    Lesson 1: Introduction and Three Foundational Issues
    Lesson 2: Understanding Anger as a Foe
    Lesson 3: Understanding Anger as a Friend
    Lesson 4: Anger is a Prompt to Create a Plan
    Lesson 5: How to Change Using an Anger Journal

4. Getting the most from this material.

Study it in a small group.

Use the study guide (and the Anger Journal).

5. Two important disclaimers.

LESSON 1
Video B: Three Foundational Issues

1. Anger is your _____ **and your** _____.

We know that not all anger is sinful because:

a. _____ was angry.

b. _____ is righteously angry.

c. God commands _____ , "In your anger do not sin."

In your anger do not sin. — Ephesians 4:26 (NIV)

To be angry with the right person, and to the right degree, and at the right time, and for the right purpose, and in the right way – that is not within everybody's power and is not easy. — Aristotle

2. Definitions of Anger

"Anger is a whole-personed active response to a negative moral judgment against a perceived evil." — Dr. Robert Jones in *Uprooting Anger: Biblical Help for a Common Problem.*[1]

Anger is *"an active stance you take to oppose something you assess as important and wrong."* — Dr. David Powlison in *Good and Angry: Redeeming Anger, Irritation, Complaining, and Bitterness.*[2]

3. Sinful anger usually comes from a blocked goal or _____.

What causes quarrels and what causes fights among you? Is it not this, that your passions are at war within you? You desire and do not have, so you murder. You covet and cannot obtain, so you fight and quarrel.
— James 4:1-2

Two Types of Desires:

The evil in our desire typically does not lie in what we want, but that we want it too much. Often the object of the desire is good, and the evil lies in the Lordship of the desire. Natural desires for good things are meant to exist subordinate to our desire to please the Giver of gifts. It's not the desire but the status of the desire."

— Dr. David Powlison

ANGER JOURNAL

One way to help you become more self-reflective about times that you get upset is to journal about each incident.[3] You can find the full journal questions in Appendix 2 and hear the teaching about them in Lesson 5.

For this week, there is space on pages 18 and 19 for you to record difficult incidents. Start this process by writing down as much as you can. Don't worry about leaving blank spaces.

 Video lessons are available for purchase at www.ApollosU.com.

DISCUSSION QUESTIONS

Use the following questions to guide your discussion.

1. What reasons were given for why we don't talk much about anger? Do you agree? Are there others you would add? Which of those ring true in your life?

2. What do you think about the statement that anger is both your foe and your friend?

3. Let's look over those two definitions of anger again.

- *"Anger is a whole-personed active response to a negative moral judgment against a perceived evil."* — Jones

- Anger is *"an active stance you take to oppose something you assess as important and wrong."* — Powlison

How do those definitions help you understand anger a little better? What in the definitions surprises you?

4. Read Mark 3:1-5. What motivated Jesus' anger? What wrong did he see? How does this contrast with Jesus' response when he was crucified? What is the implication for you?

5. Read James 4:1-2. What causes desires, fights, and quarrels to come into your family? How does that change your understanding of parenting? What do you think of this idea of good desires that can become demands in the moment? How does that help clear up your thinking? Can you give some examples of issues you are currently facing?

6. What will you take away from this discussion to apply to yourself?

Begin praying that the Lord would change you into a patient parent by the power of the Spirit.

NOTES

The Sinless Anger of Jesus

We know that not all anger is wrong. Jesus, the perfect man, never sinned, and Scripture records that he was angry. Let's review the Scriptures we looked at in the video.

Read Mark 3:1-5.

1. What prompted Jesus' anger? How did he express that anger?

2. How had God and this man been sinned against?

The Pharisees, who were supposed to speak for God, had so misinterpreted the Word that they were harming individuals. Jesus expressed his anger and grief at this injustice. His anger had the proper authority, motive, focus, and expression toward that evil.

Read Mark 11:15-18. Here is another time Jesus was probably angry.

3. What situation prompted that anger?

4. How did he express that anger?

5. How had God and others been sinned against?

6. Did Jesus have authority to do this? Why?

Again, we notice that Jesus has the right to deal with this injustice. Our goal is not to be a person who never gets angry. Anger can be given to motivate us to act against an evil. But we need to be very careful. We need to realize that, as sinful people, we pervert anger so that it is often sinful. Rarely do we completely have the right motive or expression.

7. Write out a prayer asking the Lord to help you grow in a biblical understanding of this issue as well as grow in personal awareness of your own heart.

Jesus Models Lack of Anger

While Jesus had the authority to be angry when God and others were sinned against, let's look at how he reacted when he was sinned against.

Read Matthew 27:27-44.

1. Write down all the people who sinned against Jesus. List the sinful and evil things they did to him.

2. Peter's commentary on this event is found in 1 Peter 2:22-23. Write out these verses. Jesus has the power to retaliate and take revenge. How did he respond?

3. Circle the verbs. What did Jesus do and not do? Why?

4. Write out 1 Peter 3:9 and what God commands of us.

5. Read Luke 23:34. How did Jesus do this on the cross?

6. Knowing the indwelling Spirit empowers us to follow Jesus, how do these verses cause you to love him more? How do they encourage you to fight against sin?

7. Write out a prayer asking the Lord to give you power to overcome evil with good.

Right with God

Because we know that we sin in our anger, it is absolutely vital to understand the gospel – the atoning work of Jesus on the cross. Today we are going to read another familiar passage of Scripture that will help us understand how we become right with God. Given the material we will cover in the coming weeks, the gospel must be clear in our minds.

As we look at the crucifixion of Jesus, we want to focus on the two criminals who were crucified on either side of him. At first they both insulted Jesus. But then one had a change of heart.

Read Luke 23:32-43.

1. What do you notice about the second criminal (v.40)? What did he think about his own condemnation? What did he think about the condemnation of Jesus?

2. How did this criminal show saving faith in Jesus?

3. What did Jesus promise him?

Christians throughout the centuries have understood our state to be similar to the criminals. We all are guilty before God. Like the criminals, we rightly deserve God's punishment, since the wages of sin is death (Romans 6:23).

If that is true, Jesus, a righteous man, should not have had to die. He had always perfectly pleased his Father. Instead, he should have been transfigured into heaven.

So how did that guilty criminal get into a perfect heaven? In the moment he cried out to Jesus, he became righteous before God. His sin was put on Jesus and Jesus' righteousness was put on him. Theologians call this double imputation. The criminal's sin was placed on Jesus; Jesus' righteousness was given to the repentant man. We might picture it like this:

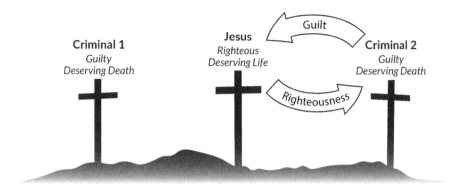

4. Paul puts the picture above into words in 2 Corinthians 5:21. Write the verse out below and see if you can see it in the picture above.

Since the first criminal never cried out in faith, it seems that his status stayed the same.

Every person will identify with one man or the other.

If, like the second criminal, you have truly cried out for Jesus to save you, then your sins have been placed on him, and his righteousness was given to you. All God's wrath for your sins has been placed on Jesus, and his righteousness has been given to you.

If you have never truly cried out, then you are more like the first criminal, who died under God's wrath.

5. If you have never truly cried out for rescue, do it now. Write out a prayer of faith and repentance. If you have cried out before, then write a prayer of thanksgiving.

Understanding the Source of Quarrels

It is so easy to blame our fights on something external – like misbehaving children. But God's Word cuts to the heart when it helps us think deeply about where disagreements come from. Let's look again at God's Word to us in the book of James.

1. Write out James 4:1-2.

2. What causes fights and quarrels (v.1)?

3. Sinful anger often comes from a blocked goal or desire. What words does James use to say this (v.2)?

4. Thinking on the desire level is somewhat complicated. There are sinful desires that we should fight against. There are also neutral and good desires. However, sometimes we turn those into demands. Let's revisit Dr. David Powlison's observation:

> The evil in our desire typically does not lie in what we want, but that we want it too much. Often the object of the desire is good, and the evil lies in the Lordship of the desire. Natural desires for good things are meant to exist subordinate to our desire to please the giver of gifts. It's not the desire but the status of the desire.

Look at the list of personal rights in Appendix 1. Which of these do you see in yourself that lead to frustration or anger?

5. Look at the last sentence of verse 2. What is one of God's solutions when we have anger?

6. Anger should be a prompt to start praying. List the things that are making you angry now. Have you been praying about those things that make you upset? Start now.

7. Let's put James 4:2 into practice. Write out a prayer asking the Lord for wisdom about how to handle several different issues that prompt you to become angry. Ask him to show you what to do.

Taking Ownership of Our Words

It is easy to blame our angry words on what someone says or does to us. But in today's reading, we are to going to see what Jesus has to say about the source of our words. Once we really understand this, it will have huge implications. We will realize that we are responsible for everything that comes out of our mouth.

Read Matthew 12:34-37.

1. What is the source of our words (vv.34-35)?

2. Because of the source mentioned in the above questions, how seriously does Jesus take our words? Write out verses 36-37.

3. Contrast what Jesus said in verses 36-37 with how seriously we take our words. Do you tend to excuse your own words? What excuses do you say in your mind or to others when angry words come out of your mouth?

4. Jesus repeats this same theme later in his ministry. Read Matthew 15:10-20. Write out verses 18-19.

5. Look back at Question 4. What is the cause of angry words? If this is true, then what do you think Jesus would say when we blame our words on someone else?

6. We will return to this idea in the next lesson. Our words reveal our hearts and defile us. Can you see how we need the forgiving and transforming work of Jesus Christ? Have you run to him to forgive you and give you the power to change? Write out a prayer below asking forgiveness for not taking ownership of your words.

ANGER
JOURNAL

Incident 1. Date_____ Time _____

1. What was the event? What was the stimulus? What were contributing factors?

2. What did I say or do? How did I react?

3. What was I desiring in the moment? Was it a sinful desire or a good desire that was a demand in the moment? What right did I feel was violated? What was I saying to myself (in my heart)?

4. What were the consequences of my anger? What did I smash or destroy?

5. Knowing that God was ruling over those circumstances, what does God say about my reactions? What do I need to remember about him, his character, and control? How can he give me help right now? How does the gospel apply specifically?

ANGER JOURNAL

Incident 2. Date_____ Time _____

1. What was the event? What was the stimulus? What were contributing factors?

2. What did I say or do? How did I react?

3. What was I desiring in the moment? Was it a sinful desire or a good desire that was a demand in the moment? What right did I feel was violated? What was I saying to myself (in my heart)?

4. What were the consequences of my anger? What did I smash or destroy?

5. Knowing that God was ruling over those circumstances, what does God say about my reactions? What do I need to remember about him, his character, and control? How can he give me help right now? How does the gospel apply specifically?

LESSON
2

Understanding Anger as Your Foe

LECTURE NOTES

LESSON 2

Video A: Anger is Your Foe – Part 1

**1. To grow in patience, you need to realize sinful anger is in the family tree of
_____ and is serious.**

> *But I tell you that anyone who is angry with his brother will be subject to
> judgment. Again, anyone who says to his brother, "Raca," is answerable
> to the Sanhedrin. But anyone who says, "You fool!" will be in danger of
> the fire of hell.* — Matthew 5:21-22 (NIV)

**2. To grow in patience, you need to recognize, take ownership, and
_____ of all the variations of anger.**

> *Get rid of all bitterness, rage and anger, brawling and slander, along with
> every form of malice.* — Ephesians 4:31 (NIV)

Ways We Blow Up	Ways We Clam Up
1.	1. Sighing, _____
2. Clamor, Shouting	2. Resentment
3.	3. Disdain
4. Unwholesome talk	4. Giving "The _____ Treatment"
5. Name calling	5.
6. Obscenity	6. Cynicism, Hardheartedness
7.	
8. Irritability	
9.	
10. Responsive Anger	

3. To grow in patience, you need to realize that your sinful anger _____
the Holy Spirit.

> *And do not grieve the Holy Spirit of God, by whom you were sealed for the day of redemption.* — Ephesians 4:30

4. To grow in patience, you need to realize that your sinful anger is driven by the _____ **not the Spirit.**

> *Now the works of the flesh are evident:... enmity, strife, jealousy, fits of anger, rivalries, dissensions, divisions...* — Galatians 5:19-20

5. To grow in patience, you need to realize that your anger will not fix the _____ **that caused you to become angry.**

> *The anger of man does not produce the righteousness of God.*
> — James 1:20

6. To grow in patience, you need to realize that your sinful anger actually _____ **the other person.**

> *Reckless words pierce like a sword, but the tongue of the wise brings healing.* — Proverbs 12:18 (NIV)

> *The tongue has the power of life and death...* — Proverbs 18:21 (NIV)

 To be angry is to destroy." – Dr. Ed Welch

Video B: Anger is Your Foe – Part 2

7. To grow in patience, you need to realize that your sinful anger _____
and _____ **be controlled.**

> *In your anger do not sin.* — Ephesians 4:26 (NIV)

> *A fool gives full vent to his anger, but a wise man keeps himself under control.* — Proverbs 29:11 (NIV)

> (See also James 1:19, 1 Corinthians 13:5, 1 Peter 2:23)

8. To grow in patience, you need to _____ **and make restitution for your sinful anger that spilled out.**

> *For out of the abundance of the heart the mouth speaks.* — Matthew 12:34 (NIV)

9. To grow in patience, as part of your restitution, you need to replace your sinful anger with _____ **and blessing.**

> *Be kind to one another, tenderhearted, forgiving one another, as God in Christ forgave you.* — Ephesians 4:32

> *Do not repay evil for evil or reviling for reviling, but on the contrary, bless, for to this you were called, that you may obtain a blessing.* — 1 Peter 3:9

10. To grow in patience, as part of your restitution, you need to come up with a specific _____.

 For every one look at self, take ten looks at Christ."
— Robert Murray McCheyne.

ANGER JOURNAL

One way to help you become more self-reflective about times that you get upset is to journal about each incident. You can find the full journal questions in Appendix 2 and hear the teaching about them in Lesson 5.

For this week, there is space on pages 38 and 39 for you to record difficult incidents. Start this process by writing down as much as you can. Don't worry about leaving blank spaces.

 Video lessons are available for purchase at www.ApollosU.com.

DISCUSSION QUESTIONS

Use the following questions to guide your discussion.

This lesson helps us see our sin in depth so that we can repent deeply.

1. How do most people excuse their anger?

2. Had you thought of sinful anger as miniature murder? If we really saw it like Jesus sees it, how would we be affected?

3. Did you find the distinction between blowing up and clamming up helpful? Can you identify with one or both? Which one of the manifestations in the list surprised you? Why? Which ones can you relate to?

4. How does our anger affect the Spirit? Had you thought about the Spirit as an ally in your fight? How does that change your perspective?

5. What did you think of the analogy of the cup of acid? Can anyone really cause us to sin? What, then, is the real cause of unedifying words?

6. What types of restitution were discussed?

7. What will you take away from this lesson and apply to yourself?

NOTES

Sinful Anger is Miniature Murder

It is easy to excuse our anger. After all, we think, "I would not have gotten angry if my _____ (husband, wife, child) had not _____."

Yet no one can make us sin.

Part of growing into Jesus-like patience is realizing the seriousness of our own sin. We must be determined to grow no matter what the other person does. Let's look again at Jesus' solemn words.

1. Write out Matthew 5:21-22.

2. Look at Jesus' serious command and warning. What is anger related to (vv.21-22)? This command comes from the Ten Commandments. You can find them in Exodus 20:1-19, especially verse 13. You can also revisit Genesis 3:3-11 to see the direct connection between anger and murder.

3. How else does anger manifest itself (v.23)?

4. Does seeing anger as miniature murder change your perspective on things? How?

5. Jesus said, "He who has been forgiven much loves much." In light of how sinful anger violates the law of love, how does this make the atoning work of Jesus even sweeter?

6. If you really saw sinful anger as Jesus sees it, what would happen in your life? Pray for that perspective, asking God to help you see it as seriously as he does.

No Trash Talking

It is so easy to excuse our words when we become angry. But God gives us a clear teaching on our words in our verses for today.

Read Ephesians 4:26-32.

1. Look at verse 26. Some versions translate this verse, "Be angry and sin not." This can sound like a command for us to become angry! Other versions translate verse 26 as "In your anger do not sin." In other words, God is telling us what to do when we become angry.[4] Or stated another way, "When you get angry, do not sin." We will focus on the second part, "Do not sin."

Based on that verse, do you believe you can control your anger and not sin?

2. The Lord never gives a command for which he doesn't also provide the strength to carry it out. How does this verse encourage you?

Consider writing Ephesians 4:26 out and posting it somewhere you can see it.

3. In Ephesians 4:29, God tells us:

> Let no corrupting talk come out of your mouths, but only such as is good for building up, as fits the occasion, that it may give grace to the hearer.

a. What is forbidden in the first part of the verse? Are there any exceptions?

b. What is the positive commanded after the word but?

such as is good for _____ _____

as fits the _____

that it may give _____ to the hearer.

c. Rewrite each of those three positive phrases in your own words. Notice how this verse speaks to the content, the timing, and the impact of our speech.

My words should...

This is a great verse to memorize. Consider posting it and memorizing it.

4. Review the past several days. Can you identify unwholesome or corrupting or "garbage" words that came out of your mouth? What were they? Don't forget to start using the Anger Journal at the end of this lesson.

5. Write out a prayer asking the Lord's forgiveness, for awareness, and for help in speaking words that give grace to others

Putting Off Anger; Putting on Kindness

We are going to continue reviewing Scriptures from our earlier video lesson. Specifically, we will focus on how our anger grieves the Spirit and what we can do to replace that anger.

Read Ephesians 4:30-32 again.

1. How does the anger of verse 31 and garbage talk of verse 29 affect the Spirit within us?

What are some other synonyms for *grieve*?

Did you realize your ability to impact the Holy Spirit that way? How would it affect your life if you really absorbed this verse?

2. Look over verse 31 below. Paul lists five manifestations of anger. Circle the ones you see in your life.

> *Let all bitterness and wrath and anger and clamor and slander be put away from you, along with all malice.*

3. If we are to put off these five things and put on others, what are we to put on? Write out some opposites of bitterness, wrath, anger, clamor, slander, and malice.

4. Verse 32 has more of the "put on." Read it and list three characteristics.

   a. Be _____ -

   b. _____ -

   c. _____ one another.

Write out what this would look like in your parenting.

5. Being kind and compassionate is not incompatible with handing out consequences. We will talk about that in Lesson 4. In the stresses of parenting, what would kindness and being tenderhearted look like in your life right now?

6. Write out a prayer confessing unwholesome talk and asking the Lord to give you words of kindness and grace that build up.

Walking by the Spirit Not the Flesh

It is so easy to justify our anger. But when we look at the manifestation of the Spirit and the manifestations of our flesh (or the remaining sinful nature) it is pretty clear where our anger comes from.

Read Galatians 5:16-26.

1. List out the works of the flesh (or sinful nature) related to anger found in verse 20. Write some short examples or definitions of these words.

2. Read verse 21. How serious is it to keep indulging in these sins? What is the warning?

3. Write out verses 22 and 23. Circle the qualities of the Spirit that are opposite of anger.

4. This whole passage sets out the contrast between two motivating forces within the believer – the Holy Spirit and the flesh. Write out verses 16-18.

5. What is the battle you are in (v.17)?

6. How do we walk in victory? What does verse 16 teach about walking in victory?

7. What does verse 18 teach about walking in obedience?

8. What does verse 25 teach about walking in obedience?

9. Can you walk by the Spirit today? What will that look like?

10. Write out a prayer asking the Holy Spirit to empower you to meet the challenges of the day with love and joy.

Slow to Anger

Today's study takes us to another passage that speaks to parents with children of all ages.

1. Write out James 1:19-20.

2. What are the three commands in the passage? Circle them.

3. What reason does God give for being slow to anger (v.20)?

4. Think deeply about the last time you became angry—even in your mind—without barking at someone. Your sinful anger was trying to accomplish something. What was it?

5. According to verse 20, did it? How does that motivate you to grow in patience?

6. Read Exodus 34:6-7. This is an oft-repeated passage (see Numbers 14:18, Psalm 86:15, 103:8, 145:8), where God discloses himself to Moses. What do you learn about God's character?

7. God was often slow to anger with the Israelites Can you think of ways God has been slow to anger with you? Can you list them?

8. Can you extend that same grace to others? What would you think of a person who had received so much patience from God but couldn't show it to others?

9. How does God's patience (or longsuffering) motivate your own growth in this area with your children? Write out a prayer asking God to reveal how patient he has been and continues to be with you.

ANGER JOURNAL

Incident 1. Date_____ Time _____

1. What was the event? What was the stimulus? What were contributing factors?

2. What did I say or do? How did I react?

3. What was I desiring in the moment? Was it a sinful desire or a good desire that was a demand in the moment? What right did I feel was violated? What was I saying to myself (in my heart)?

4. What were the consequences of my anger? What did I smash or destroy?

5. Knowing that God was ruling over those circumstances, what does God say about my reactions? What do I need to remember about him, his character, and control? How can he give me help right now? How does the gospel apply specifically?

ANGER
JOURNAL

Incident 1. Date_____ Time _____

1. What was the event? What was the stimulus? What were contributing factors?

2. What did I say or do? How did I react?

3. What was I desiring in the moment? Was it a sinful desire or a good desire that was a demand in the moment? What right did I feel was violated? What was I saying to myself (in my heart)?

4. What were the consequences of my anger? What did I smash or destroy?

5. Knowing that God was ruling over those circumstances, what does God say about my reactions? What do I need to remember about him, his character, and control? How can he give me help right now? How does the gospel apply specifically?

LESSON 3

Understanding Anger as Your Friend

LECTURE NOTES

LESSON 3:

Video A: Anger is Your Friend

1. Anger can be used to indicate a _____.

2. Anger should motivate us to attack the _____ not the _____.

> *In your anger do not sin.* — Ephesians 4:26

Diagram 1 (To be completed during the video)[5]

Parent   Child

Diagram 2

Parent   Child

Diagram 3

Parent   Child

3. Anger should motivate us to come up with a _____.

Video B: Anger is a Prompt to Create a Plan for Your Heart

1. You can become more patient by looking at you own _____ with Christ.

2. You can become more patient by knocking over the _____ and _____ in your heart.

> *Truly, truly, I say to you, unless a grain of wheat falls into the earth and dies, it remains alone; but if it dies, it bears much fruit.* — John 12:24

> **The Parenting Paradox**
> We expect our children to obey because God commands it. We expect our children to disobey because they are sinful."

3. You can become more patient by praying for _____.

> *You do not have, because you do not ask God.* — James 4:2

4. You can become more patient by coming up with a specific _____
plan.

Doors of Escape

    a. Keep _____ and pray (Matthew 26:41).

    b. Verbalize specific_____ (Ephesians 6:17).

    c. Walk by the _____ (Romans 8:13, Galatians 5:16).

    d. _____ (2 Timothy 2:22).

    e. Pursue righteousness with _____ (2 Timothy 2:22).

Sin demands to have a man by himself. It withdraws him from the community. The more isolated a person is, the more destructive will be the power of sin over him, and the more deeply he becomes involved in it, the more disastrous is the isolation. Sin wants to remain unknown. It shuns the light."
— Dietrich Bonhoeffer.[6]

ANGER JOURNAL

This week's lesson includes the full set of journal questions on page 58. Fill them in as much as you can. Don't worry about leaving blank spaces.

 Video lessons are available for purchase at www.ApollosU.com.

DISCUSSION QUESTIONS

Use the following questions to guide your discussion.

This lesson helps us see that our anger is given to motivate us to act. As Dr. David Powlison has said, "Not getting angry can, in fact, be an anger problem."

1. What do you think about the idea of anger as the red light on the dashboard given to indicate a problem?

2. Let's review the diagrams.

   a. What does the first diagram indicate about the wrong way to attack a problem? Give some examples of wrong ways we do this.

   b. What does the second diagram indicate about the right way to attack a problem? Does this diagram change your perspective? How? How might you put this in practice?

   c. "Our children are never the problem; their sin is." What do you think about that sentence? If we really got that into our heads, how would we change?

   d. Do you have older children? How does the third diagram help you?

3. Focusing on our hearts starts with focusing on Christ. As you contemplate his patience with those who persecuted and tortured him, how does that give you confidence his Spirit can develop a similar patience in you?

4. What is the parenting paradox? How could that help you overcome your anger? Do you tend to parent on cruise control? How does the parenting paradox change that?

5. What do you think about the idea of having specific emergency doors of escape? Which ones could you see implementing? How? What verses will you use to encourage you to remain patient?

6. What will you take away from this discussion that you will apply to yourself?

NOTES

Knocking Over the Idols

My Hindu friend lives in a typical suburban house. In the middle of the house, off the kitchen, is the pantry closet. But opening the door doesn't reveal extra food and odd- shaped cookware. Instead this closet contains her shrine. In it are numerous small idols as well as different religious paraphernalia. Unseen to the outside world, this idol closet is an important part of her life, her worship, and her outlook.

In a similar way, each Christian has idols and an idol closet as well. The idols are mental not metal. And the "closet" is in our hearts.

We all have intense desires that drive us more than our love for Christ. Or to put it another way, we all hold on to "rights" that we think we have. And when those rights are trampled, we become angry. Anger often reveals idols.

1. Look again at the list of personal rights in Appendix 1. Which of those idols/ rights create anger most often in your day? List four or five that you see in your life.

2. Part of following Christ involves proper death to self. Read John 12:23-26. Jesus is referring to his impending death on the cross. What did he say about it (vv.23-24)?

3. Does this principle apply to Jesus' followers as well? Are we to imitate this death to self (vv.24-25)?

4. How does this death to self involve giving up the perceived rights you listed above in Question 1?

5. Read Philippians 2:5-8. We are told to have the mind of Christ. What did he do or not do?

Verse 6

Verse 7

Verse 8

6. What did God do (v.9)?

7. How can properly dying to your rights help you become more patient?

8. Write out a prayer asking the Lord to help you do this.

*This is a good place to remind you that even as Scripture urges you to deny yourself for the sake of serving others, it is never, ever right for someone to be abusive in their relationship with you. The call of this day's devotional in the context of parenting younger (or even teen) children is different than your relationship with your spouse. Normal suffering can become destructive suffering. God has given us instructions about how to handle other adults who repeatedly sin against us without repentance (see Matt 18:15ff.).

Temptation

As we have seen from Ephesians 4:26, anger can be a temptation to sin. However, just because we are tempted does not mean we have to give way to sin. The Bible has much to say about the subject of temptation. Let's look at a key verse about this subject.

> *No temptation has overtaken you that is not common to man. God is faithful, and he will not let you be tempted beyond your ability, but with the temptation he will also provide the way of escape, that you may be able to endure it.* —1 Corinthians 10:13

This verse is made up of three significant sentences or clauses. Fill in the blank below with the rest of the sentence from the verse.

1. No temptation has _____

_____ .

a. Do you sometimes hesitate to reveal temptation because you think you are the only one who struggles with it and that other people don't? How does this sentence encourage you?

b. Paul describes temptation as overtaking us. If you really thought of temptation as a fight, how would it change your perspective?

2. God is faithful, and he will not _____

_____ .

a. What is the promise in this part of the verse?

b. Do you sometimes feel your circumstances are too much? How does this verse correct that thinking?

3. But with the temptation _____

_____ .

a. What does God do in the midst of temptation?

b. Can you think of a current temptation and current way of escape you see?

4. Diamonds are formed by tremendous pressure. In a similar way, standing up under trials and temptations transforms your character. Write out a prayer asking the Lord to help you grow in standing up under the temptations that come.

The Sword of the Spirit

We really are in a spiritual battle. The devil wants to tempt us to sin against God and injure others. But we are not defenseless! The Lord has given us powerful weapons to help in the spiritual battle. In this well-known passage, we will look at parts of our spiritual armor and how to use them.

Read Ephesians 6:10-18.

1. What is the piece of armor mentioned in the first part of verse 16? What does it help us do?

2. How have you seen faith help fight off negative or tempting thoughts?

3. What piece of armor is mentioned at the end of verse 17? How can verbalizing specific scriptures or posting specific scriptures help you fight temptation?

4. Look at Matthew 4:1-4. Jesus is both our Savior and our example. What do you notice about how he fights temptation?

5. Review the verses covered so far in this study. Choose several commands and several promises that you will speak to yourself and post around your house. Which ones will you choose? Consider looking at Proverbs 29:11, Ephesians 4:26, James 1:19-20, Ephesians 4:29, Galatians 5:22-23, 1 Corinthians 10:13. Post it now!

6. Write out a prayer asking the Lord to help you hold up the shield of faith in one hand and the sword of the Spirit in the other.

Expectations and Frustrations

Some situations are nobody's fault. We live in a fallen world where things break, work is hard, and people are unpredictable. It can cause frustration. We don't often think of frustration as anger. But it is. In today's reading, we are going to look at Martha's situation and frustration for insight into our own hearts and situations beyond our control.

Read Luke 10:38-42.

1. Martha welcomed Jesus and his disciples into her home (v.38). Perhaps with little notice, she was suddenly hosting at least 13 men for dinner. If this happened to you, what would you be thinking needed to be done?

2. Since Mary, Martha's sister, lived with her, what were Martha's expectations? How does Martha's frustration express itself (v.40)?

3. Martha seems to be the homeowner and responsible one while Mary seems to be the more carefree. What temptation does Jesus observe about Martha (v.41)?

4. Are you a responsible one like Martha? What logistics cause you frustration and anger? How do you express it? To whom do you express it? How do you tend to excuse it?

5. What would Spirit-filled patience and joy look like in that moment?

6. Revisit the list of personal rights in Appendix 1. Which one of those rights, expectations, or idols might Martha have had? Which ones cause you frustration?

7. Write out a prayer asking the Lord to grow you in patience and joy no matter what situation comes your way.

Flee with Friends

We were never made to live the Christian life alone. As we saw all the way back in our introduction, anger can be a secret sin because often no one sees us when we're angry. In today's passage, we are going to look at one of the many places that Scripture calls us to pursue godliness with others.

1. Write out 2 Timothy 2:22.

2. We are often told to flee from sin. (See also 1 Corinthians 6:18, 10:14, 1 Timothy 6:11). If you are upset with your children, what are some very practical ways you could separate yourself in the moment? Write out all the ways you can think of.

3. How will this separation allow you to call upon the help of the Spirit and take up the sword of the Spirit? What will you call to mind in that moment?

4. The rest of verse 22 encourages us to pursue righteousness with others who are pursuing righteousness. Who knows about this area you are working on? You need their help and they need yours. How can you connect with them about this issue?

5. Read through the following quotation from Dietrich Bonhoeffer. Underline or circle key sentences for you.

> He who is alone with his sin is utterly alone. It may be that Christians, notwithstanding corporate worship, common prayer, and all their fellowship in service, may still be left in their loneliness. The final break-through to fellowship does not occur, because they have fellowship with one another as believers and as devout people, they do not have fellowship as the undevout, as sinners.
>
> The pious fellow permits no one to be a sinner. So everybody must conceal his sin from himself and the fellowship. We dare not be sinners. Many Christians are unthinkably horrified when a real sinner is suddenly discovered among the righteous. So we remain alone with our sin, living in lies and hypocrisy ...
>
> In confession the breakthrough to community takes place ... In confession the light of the Gospel breaks into the darkness and seclusion of the heart.[7]

6. In Ephesians 4:26 God commands us, "[D]o not let the sun go down on your anger." How does that fit with fleeing? Read *Should You Let the Sun Go Down on Your Anger?* (Appendix 5). Can you see the wisdom there? Do you agree? Why or why not?

7. Write out a prayer asking the Lord for people to whom you can be open and honest. Then ask him for the courage to talk with them!

ANGER JOURNAL

This week we are including the full Anger Journal. For help filling it out, view Lesson 5.

Incident 1. Date_____ Time _____

The Foolish Circle of Folly

1. What was the event? What was the stimulus? What were contributing factors?

2. What did I say or do? How did I react?

3. What was I desiring in the moment? Was it a sinful desire or a good desire that was a demand in the moment? What right did I feel was violated? What was I saying to myself (in my heart)?

4. What were the consequences of my anger? What did I smash or destroy?

5. Knowing that God was ruling over those circumstances, what does God say about my reactions? What do I need to remember about him, his character, and control? How can he give me help right now? How does the gospel apply specifically?

The Gracious Circle of Wisdom

6. How would God have me act in the circumstance? How can I glorify God in the future when this situation comes up? How can I call on him for help?

7. What should rule my heart when that circumstance comes up?

8. How do I need to undo the harm? How should I confess and repent?

9. What plan should I make for my heart or the situation so this will not happen again? How can I attack the problem not the person? Should I do one or more of these: pray, forbear, bring up when a better time, come up with a plan, seek wise counsel?

10. What verses will I use to renew my mind and remind me of this temptation? How will I bring this situation before the Lord in prayer, seeking his wisdom? (James 1:2-5)

LESSON 4

Anger is a Prompt to Create a Plan

LECTURE NOTES

Video A: Anger is a Prompt to Create a Plan for Your Parenting - Part 1

1. Take time to think about the parenting _____
you are facing.

2. Take time to create a _____.

3. Use _____ instead of words.

God has given you two tools:

    Words (Positive and Corrective)

    Actions (Positive and Corrective)

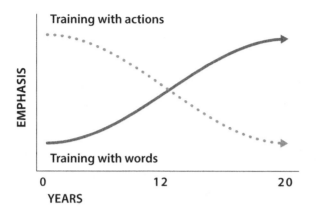

 Say what you mean and mean what you say."

LESSON 4:

Video B: Anger is a Prompt to Create a Plan for Your Parenting - Part 2

4. Reexamine the _____ you are giving your children.

Rules without relationship leads to rebellion. — Josh McDowell

But...

Relationship without rules leads to chaos. — Chap Bettis

5. Add _____ to your parenting time.

6. Make use of your _____ community.

7. Actively _____ .

(Plus a Quick Reminder) Pray for _____ .

ANGER JOURNAL

This week's lesson includes the full set of journal questions on page 78. Fill them in as much as you can. Don't worry about leaving blank spaces.

 Video lessons are available for purchase at www.ApollosU.com.

DISCUSSION QUESTIONS

Use the following questions to guide your discussion.

1. Dr. David Powlison says:

> Anger done right is a great good. It says, "That's wrong" and energizes
> us to address real problems.... It is an active stance you take to oppose
> something that you assess as both important and wrong. You notice
> something, size it up, and say, "That matters... and it's not right."[8]

Do you agree or disagree with this statement? How does this quotation help you
channel appropriate anger?

2. Both of the first two principles deal with taking time. Do you have a time
when you calmly and formally talk about family issues you are facing? What do
you think of the idea of a coffee date? (See Appendix 3 for the article. You will
read it later this week in your devotional time.)

3. Review the eight suggestions. Which seem applicable to your situation? What
would change look like for you?

4. One of the suggestions was to reexamine the freedoms you are giving your
children. How does this good desire backfire on parents? Have you seen this in
your home?

5. Brainstorm with the group to come up with some wise older parents in your
church community who you think would give wise advice. If you needed to go
outside your church, who could you go to?

6. What will you take away from this discussion and apply to yourself?

NOTES

Making Plans

Please note that this is not a full parenting course. We are going to only touch lightly on the specific how-to principles here. For more specific instruction, explore the *Parenting with Confidence* course produced by our ministry or the recommended resources at the beginning of this workbook.

1. Write out Proverbs 21:5.

What are the types of people contrasted? Do you think this applies to parenting? What are the parenting outcomes that usually result?

2. Write out Proverbs 15:22.

What is being encouraged in this verse?

3. Write out Proverbs 16:3.

What is being encouraged in this verse?

4. Write out Isaiah 32:8.

What does God say about a noble person?

5. Write out Isaiah 33:22.

This verse shows the three roles the Lord has over his realm. What does each do? How do parents imitate him? Can you see the value of calmly calling the legislature (rule-making body) in this session and making rules for your family?

6. Read *The Power of the Coffee Date* (Appendix 3). Do you think this would work for you? What benefits might there be? If you resist this idea, what is the reason? What barriers might you encounter to make this happen? If you are a single parent, would it be helpful to do this with another parent? Who?

7. Write out a prayer asking the Lord to help you become a wise person who makes noble plans for your parenting.

Servant and Authority

Today we want to look at a biblical tension. As parents we are both sinful individuals and God's authorities. We are co-regents, ruling with delegated authority from the Lord. We are servants and leaders. If we don't exercise that authority, we are not humble and loving; we are disobedient. Let's examine these thoughts more closely.

1. Read John 13:3-17. What did Jesus do for his disciples? What did he want them to learn about serving in the kingdom?

2. Read Matthew 20:25-28. How is greatness achieved in the kingdom? How is Jesus our example (v.28)?

3. Read Acts 6:1-4. Even though Jesus had washed their feet and told them to do the same, how did the disciples handle this problem in the congregation? What does that tell you about their understanding of godly and wise leadership?

4. Some parents, understanding the need to have a servant heart, inadvertently become child-centered. They do everything for their child and don't ask for or expect obedience as an authority. Do you find it harder to serve or to exercise authority? Why?

5. Write out Ephesians 6:4.

6. Circle the verbs in the previous verse. Is this a verse a command or a suggestion? What implication does that have for your parenting?

7. In *The Disciple-Making Parent*, I wrote this:

> As parents we have real, God-given authority. Our authority is a delegation of God's authority. For the sake of our small children, we literally stand in the place of our Heavenly Father. To disobey us is to disobey God. If we are not correcting their disobedience and if we look lightly upon it, we are in fact training them to disobey us. If, by our neglect, we are training them to disobey us, then we are actually training our children to develop a character that will disobey God later.

> J. C. Ryle made a similar observation many years ago:

>> You must not wonder that men refuse to obey their Father which is in heaven, if you allow them, when children, to disobey their father who is upon the earth.[9]

> As stewards, you do not discipline your children for your own peace and quiet. You train them to say "Yes" to you so that later they will find it easier to follow their Heavenly Father. We impose restrictions when they are little so that later they will joyfully embrace the restrictions of their Heavenly Father (Psalm 119:32). If we let them ignore and disobey authority when they are young, why are so surprised that they disregard the ultimate authority later?[10]

Underline or circle the sentences that seem most important to you.*

8. Write out a prayer asking the Lord to give you a heart of service and a heart that exercises proper authority well.

*For your free audiobook of *The Disciple-Making Parent* or to receive regular parenting encouragement from the ministry simply send an email to audiobook@theapollosproject.com with *Parenting with Patience* in the subject line.

Consequences

All of us respond to consequences. Think of how a speeding ticket motivates changes in behavior!

1. Read *A Parable of Two Kind Police Officers* (Appendix 4). What was their problem? Can you identify with their problem? Do you have the same difficulty with your children?

2. What do you think about the solution?

3. What "laws" are being broken in your household that prompt you to get upset? Write them down so that you can see them.

4. Write out Proverbs 29:19. What does this teach about the need for consequences? How does that apply to our parenting?

5. Which of these four statements apply in your situation?

I am afraid to hand out painful consequences. I don't want to hurt my children.

I am afraid to hand out painful consequences. I want my children to like me.

The consequences are not working.

I don't know what to give as a consequence.

How should you correct your thinking? Write those truths here.

6. Who has wisdom that could help you with the above problems? Will you talk with them?

7. Write out a prayer asking for the willingness to hand out training consequences in love.

The Character Chart

God is not a distant father. He is actively involved in the lives of his children. Read the following verses from the New Testament to gain a new perspective on God's work. The following verses show us that correction is part of God's love. This can motivate your parenting as you emulate him.

1. Read Hebrews 12:5-11. Write out verse 6.

2. Does the Lord sometimes give his children unpleasant consequences? Is it because he loves us or hates us? (See also Revelation 3:19.)

3. Write out Hebrews 12:11.

4. What are some characteristics of the Lord's correction in our lives? What implication does that have for our parenting?

5. Read 2 Thessalonians 3:10. What were the wrong actions of these Christians? What solution or consequence did Paul prescribe?

6. Let's reverse this principle. What is the natural consequence for working hard?

7. One way to keep track of consequences is to think about natural or artificial consequences that come with the misbehavior. Read *The Character Chart* (Appendix 6). Would that work in your house? Tomorrow we will fill one in.

8. Write out a prayer asking the Lord to help you be his representative in bringing loving correction to your children.

Filling in the Character Chart

Today we are going to create a plan and communicate it with our children.

1. Read James 1:5-8. What are we encouraged to do when we lack wisdom? What is the promise in this verse? Write a prayer for wisdom.

2. In column 1, make a list of the problems that have caused you to become angry in the past weeks or before the course began.

Problem	Corrective Consequence or Positive Motivation

3. Now, in column 2, begin brainstorming on different solutions. One type of solution might be to have a corrective consequence. Another solution would be to have a positive reward.

Here are some examples:

Problem	Corrective Consequence or Positive Motivation
Interrupting	Isolation for 3 minutes and then retry
Lots of "potty talk"	Clean the potty
Getting out of bed at night	Giving music or story that is taken away
Complaining about a chore	An extra chore

4. Have you talked with your spouse about your solutions? Have you invited other input from wise parents in your church? What did they suggest?

5. When you are filling out the Character Chart, ask yourself, "Am I willing to implement these consistently? Or are they idle threats?"

6. Fill in the Character Chart found in Appendix 6 and inform your children that you are going to start implementing these.

7. Commit your plan to the Lord. Ask him: to help you communicate it well, to give you the courage to carry it out, and to guide you in changing it as needed. However, remember to continue to pray for your own heart. We all know that a plan itself will not solve our heart problem!

ANGER
JOURNAL

This week we are including the full Anger Journal. For help filling it out, view Lesson 5.

Incident 1. Date_____ Time _____

The Foolish Circle of Folly

1. What was the event? What was the stimulus? What were contributing factors?

2. What did I say or do? How did I react?

3. What was I desiring in the moment? Was it a sinful desire or a good desire that was a demand in the moment? What right did I feel was violated? What was I saying to myself (in my heart)?

4. What were the consequences of my anger? What did I smash or destroy?

5. Knowing that God was ruling over those circumstances, what does God say about my reactions? What do I need to remember about him, his character, and control? How can he give me help right now? How does the gospel apply specifically?

The Gracious Circle of Wisdom

6. How would God have me act in the circumstance? How can I glorify God in the future when this situation comes up? How can I call on him for help?

7. What should rule my heart when that circumstance comes up?

8. How do I need to undo the harm? How should I confess and repent?

9. What plan should I make for my heart or the situation so this will not happen again? How can I attack the problem not the person? Should I do one or more of these: pray, forbear, bring up when a better time, come up with a plan, seek wise counsel?

10. What verses will I use to renew my mind and remind me of this temptation? How will I bring this situation before the Lord in prayer, seeking his wisdom? (James 1:2-5)

LESSON 5

How to Change Using an Anger Journal

LECTURE NOTES

Video A: Understanding the Cycle of Change

But that is not the way you learned Christ! – assuming that you have heard of him and were taught in him, as the truth that is in Jesus, to put off your old self, which belongs to your former manner of life and is corrupt through deceitful desires, and to be renewed in the spirit of your minds, and to put on the new self – created after the likeness of God in true righteousness and holiness. — Ephesians 4:20-24

put _____ the old self...

be renewed in the spirit of your minds...

put _____ the new self...

The Precursor - _____

The Four Steps of Change

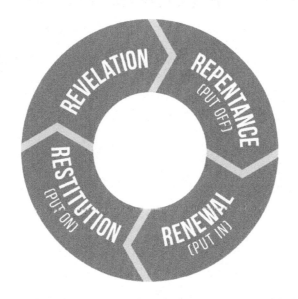

1. R_____

2. R_____ [Put off]

3. Renewal [Put _____]

4. Restitution [Put _____]

Video B: Using the Anger Journal to Change

The Foolish Circle of Folly

1. What was the event? What was the stimulus? What were contributing factors?

2. What did I say or do? How did I react?

3. What was I desiring in the moment? Was it a sinful desire or a good desire that was a demand in the moment? What right did I feel was violated? What was I saying to myself (in my heart)?

4. What were the consequences of my anger? What did I smash or destroy?

5. Knowing that God was ruling over those circumstances, what does God say about my reactions? What do I need to remember about him, his character, and control? How can he give me help right now? How does the gospel apply specifically?

The Gracious Circle of Wisdom

6. How would God have me act in the circumstance? How can I glorify God in the future when this situation comes up? How can I call on him for help?

7. What should rule my heart when that circumstance comes up?

8. How do I need to undo the harm? How should I confess and repent?

9. What plan should I make for my heart or the situation so this will not happen again? How can I attack the problem not the person? Should I do one or more of these: pray, forbear, bring up when a better time, come up with a plan, seek wise counsel?

10. What verses will I use to renew my mind and remind me of this temptation? How will I bring this situation before the Lord in prayer, seeking his wisdom? (James 4:2, 1:2-5)

Video lessons are available for purchase at www.ApollosU.com.

DISCUSSION QUESTIONS

Use the following questions to guide your discussion.

1. What does regeneration mean? Why is it a necessary precursor?

2. Without looking back at your notes, can you name the four parts of personal change? What does each mean?

3. Scripture gives numerous examples of this concept of putting off and putting on. (For example, Roman 13:13-14 and Colossians 3 have clear *put off* and *put on* language.) As a group, fill in the chart below from a short passage in Ephesians.

	Put Off	Put On
Ephesians 4:25		
Ephesians 4:28		
Ephesians 4:29		

4. We are going to use the journal as a way to slow down and reflect on our actions and reactions. Do you think this will be helpful to you? Why or why not?

5. Read Proverbs 14:8. Look in the first part of the verse. What does the wise person do? From the second part of the verse, what can sin do to us? How does self-reflection in journaling help us become wise?

6. Look through the journal questions. Are there any you do not understand?

NOTES

Recalling the Change Process

Read Ephesians 4:20-24 again.

1. Can you can fill in the four parts of personal change? You can use the key words from verses 22-24. Look back to your previous notes if you need help.

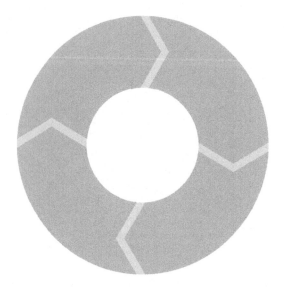

2. Can you give an example of how each of these might work in your life?

a. Revelation – I know I need to grow in becoming more patient. My spouse has said a few things to me, and my children look at me with wide eyes. I feel shame. God is getting my attention to work on it.

b. R_____ [Put _____]

c. R_____ [Put _____]

d. R _____ [Put _____]

3. Read Romans 13:14. This passage reverses the order so that it is a put on first and then a put off. Are there any ways you need to apply this verse today? If you really "put on the Lord Jesus Christ" how would that change your day?

4. Read Romans 12:1-2. Write out verse 2.

5. This is a well-known verse. What pressure do we face? How do we counter that pressure and change on the inside?

6. Look up Psalm 1:1-2 and Psalm 119:11. What is true of the godly person? Have you seen the power of God's Word to change your thinking in an area of life? How?

7. Pray and ask the Lord to begin giving you clarity about how to change in this (and other) areas.

Getting the Log Out of Our Eye

It is easy to excuse our sin by blaming others. Jesus had some good words to remind us that we tend to minimize our own sin and maximize the sin of others. The Anger Journal is meant to help you with your sin—not your spouse's sin!

1. Read Matthew 7:3-5. Write out verse 3.

2. What universal tendency is Jesus highlighting here (v.3)?

3. What command does he give to us (v.5)?

4. How does this command apply to our sin of anger? Do you find yourself thinking about someone else's need for this material?

5. Paul Tripp has said, "My view of myself is about as accurate as a fun-house mirror." Do you agree or disagree? Do these verses support that statement? If you really internalized this statement, what would change in your life?

6. In this day and age, we need to look at an important counterbalancing principle. Some, who may be the victims of mistreatment, would put all the responsibility on themselves. They would misread the above verses and think their spouse's anger is their fault.

Read Matthew 18:15-17. While we do not have space to go into this verse's important teaching in depth, let's look at it quickly.

a. When one Christian sins against another Christian, what three steps does Jesus give so that we can try and resolve the problem?

b. If you are experiencing this kind of mistreatment, Jesus commands you to bring others into the situation. How does that change your perspective? Who could you trust with this information?

7. Write out a prayer asking the Lord to help you really see your sin as he does.

Patience in Proverbs

A goal of this study is to have you grow in wisdom. Part of that wisdom is to look closely at your own life first before pointing to others. Use these verses to repent of sin, rejoice in forgiveness, and request growth.

1. Write out Proverbs 29:11.

This is an important verse. What does God teach you about your ability to control yourself?

2. Write out Proverbs 16:32.

What does this Scripture say about ruling your spirit?

3. Write out Proverbs 19:11.

What does Scripture teach about being slow to anger? The second part of the verse tells us one way. What is it?

4. Write out Proverbs 17:27.

What does God say about patience? What is implied about the foolish person?

5. Write out Proverbs 15:1.

If you find yourself in the midst of a conflict, how can you calm it? What are some examples of gentle words?

6. "For every one look at self, take ten looks at Christ." (Robert Murray McCheyne). Let's finish today's devotional by focusing on the complete forgiveness and love of our Savior. Read Romans 8:31-33. How do these verses encourage you as you seek to become more like Jesus?

7. Write a summary paragraph of what you learned. Include a prayer for God's help for growth.

Love is...

Today we are going to look at a well-known passage and apply it to our growth in patience.

Read 1 Corinthians 13:4-7.

1. Read verse 4. Write out the five characteristics of love. Then write out the opposite.

Love is...	The Opposite is...
a.	
b.	
c.	
d.	
e.	

2. Read verse 5. What are four more characteristics of love? Again, write out the opposite.

Love is...	The Opposite is...
a.	
b.	
c.	
d.	

3. Pray through the qualities in the left columns. Circle the ones that stick out to you. Ask the Lord to grow those Christ-like qualities in you.

4. Look over the qualities in the right columns. Had you thought of these as unloving? Circle the ones where you need to grow.

5. Read verses 6 and 7. Use your own words to describe other facets of love in the space below. How does this understanding impact your life?

6. Write a summary paragraph of what Jesus-likeness looks like in your situation. Include a paragraph of repentance, rejoicing in God's provision of strength and requesting growth.

7. Look back over that list of expressions of love. Do you need to ask forgiveness of someone?

8. Write out a prayer asking the Lord to grow you into a more loving person no matter what others do.

Proverbs on Listening and Asking Questions

The greatest communication skill is not talking, but listening and asking good questions. Read these verses for insight into this area. How might asking good questions de-escalate a disagreement?

1. Write out Proverbs 18:13.

What does God say about speaking without listening? Do you do this in anger?

2. Write out Proverbs 18:2.

What does this verse say about the fool? How does this contribute to anger? What is implied that a wise person would do?

3. Write out Proverbs 20:5.

What is true of a person's thoughts and motives? What does the person of understanding do? How does anger sabotage this?

4. Write out Proverbs 15:18.

What is the contrast of two types of people? Have you seen this characteristic of you at times? What was the result? What would God have you do?

5. Write out Proverbs 20:3.

What does this verse say about not arguing? What is the application for you?

6. Write a summary paragraph and prayer, asking the Lord to help you put off poor communication and put on good communication.

FINAL THOUGHTS

Dear brother or sister in the Lord,

Thank you for entrusting your time to me and studying through this material. I pray it has transformed the way you look at this issue of anger in parenting. God has given us children, not only for our happiness, but for our holiness. As we seek to follow Jesus, he will bring situations into our lives to grow us to become more and more like our patient Savior.

A second reason we are motivated to grow is because God has given us children who are eternal souls to influence for his glory. We want our homes to reflect the gospel. In addition, we want to disciple our children to the best of our ability. After all, what is more important than our children's souls?

Please feel free to reach out and tell me how the material impacted you. And please tell others. You just might change their eternity.

Chap Bettis

Appendices

APPENDIX 1
Personal Rights List

John Calvin said, "Our hearts are idols factories." Idols can be metal or mental. Though hidden much of time, conflict and anger often reveal those idols.

The following list can help you identify some of the idols of your heart. [11] Another way we might see these idols is to think of rights that we consciously or unconsciously believe we have. In particular this list will focus on conflicts around the home. You could extend the list into other areas such as work, in-laws, church, health, etc. For our purpose, we will focus on family and parenting.

Which of these rights do you consider to be "your rights?"

Right to be free of intense problems and pressure.

Right to privacy.

Right not to be bothered.

Right to be treated fairly, not to be treated unfairly.

Right to have children, to not be childless.

Right to be obeyed by my children.

Right to have healthy children.

Right to have a loving, caring, spiritually mature spouse.

Right to raise children the way I choose.

Right to have a problem free home.

Right to be on time to events.

Right to stay on my schedule.

Right to have children who work hard and succeed at school/job/marriage.

Right to hold and express personal opinions.

Right to have money/possessions and use them as I choose.

Right to plan my daily schedule.

Right to be respected, appreciated, considered important.

Right to have friends, close relationships.

Right to be loved and accepted.

Right to be understood and listened to.

Right to be supported and cared for.

Right to make my own decisions.

Right to plan my future.

Right to sexual fulfillment.

Right to fulfillment of my personal hopes and dreams.

Right to be treated fairly.

Right to have fun in life.

Right to financial security and prosperity.

Right to _____

Right to _____

Right to _____

APPENDIX 2
The Anger Journal

The Foolish Circle of Folly

1. What was the event? What was the stimulus? What were contributing factors?

2. What did I say or do? How did I react?

3. What was I desiring in the moment? Was it a sinful desire or a good desire that was a demand in the moment? What right did I feel was violated? What was I saying to myself (in my heart)?

4. What were the consequences of my anger? What did I smash or destroy?

5. Knowing that God was ruling over those circumstances, what does God say about my reactions? What do I need to remember about him, his character, and control? How can he give me help right now? How does the gospel apply specifically?

The Gracious Circle of Wisdom

6. How would God have me act in the circumstance? How can I glorify God in the future when this situation comes up? How can I call on him for help?

7. What should rule my heart when that circumstance comes up?

8. How do I need to undo the harm? How should I confess and repent?

9. What plan should I make for my heart or the situation so this will not happen again? How can I attack the problem not the person? Should I do one more of these: pray, forbear, bring up when a better time, come up with a plan, seek wise counsel?

10. What verses will I use to renew my mind and remind me of this temptation? How will I bring this situation before the Lord in prayer, seeking his wisdom? (James 4:2, 1:2-5)

APPENDIX 3

The Power of the Coffee Date

What if I told you of one simple activity that could decrease conflict and increase unity in your home? In fact, it's not an exaggeration to say that this habit has been a huge blessing to my marriage.

When Sharon and I were starting out, we wanted to be intentional about our parenting. Thanks to some good teaching, we had a great start. Then the Lord started adding more children to our family every two years. With a six-year-old, a four-year-old, a two-year-old, and a newborn, our house became increasingly chaotic. We found ourselves starting to disagree more and more.

Why the Problems?

As we stepped back and analyzed it, we realized that while the issues were becoming more complex, our time and energy to discuss them was decreasing. Earlier we used to discuss certain issues over dinner or before we went to bed. Now we could barely get a word in at dinner, and we were collapsing into bed at night.

It was about this time that a friend shared a plan that had helped his family. And indeed, I found that it was a lifesaver for us.

It was a regular coffee date.

For years, Sharon and I had a regular coffee date. I look back on this as one of the best investments in our marriage. Setting aside this time enabled me to hear my wife's heart, listen to what she was dealing with at home, and chart plans for us in the future.

Shepherds Need to Meet

Think with me a little about this. I have served for 30 years as a pastor with other elders. What helps us care for the flock together? Regular meetings of the shepherds. This habitual time enables and causes us to think about the status of the church as a whole and of individual sheep. It allows the full-time pastors to get the input of those who are not. And it "forces" the non-vocational elders to think about the status of the church.

You and your wife are shepherds of your own little flock. Men, you are supposed to be leading this flock while delegating much of the day-to-day responsibility to her. How will you regularly keep aware of the issues? How will she regularly feel your support? Regular meetings!

While I know that every couple does not have to do this, I do know many couples that would benefit.

The How-To

Here are the details that helped my wife and me.

1. We had a small notebook in the kitchen to write down the things we wanted to talk about on this date. There were several benefits to this. It allowed both of us to write down decisions we needed to make or problems we needed to talk about. For example, if we saw a new behavior pattern in one child, we didn't have to bring it up in the moment. We could just write it down to be talked about. A second benefit was that both of us could preview the list before we went out. This meant that if we were going to talk about a touchy subject, at least we had some warning to steel ourselves.

2. We had the day marked regularly in our calendar. At times our coffee date was weekly, and at other times it was every two weeks. This meant that this important time didn't get squeezed out by other activities. Or if it did get replaced, at least we realized it.

3. We *went out* for coffee. Our babysitter, who lived next door, could easily walk over to our house. If the babysitter is a logistical or financial challenge for you, consider trading off babysitting with another couple. It was important for us to get out of the house.

4. We started with prayer. When we went out, we prayed together in the car to start our evening.

5. We talked through the notebook. In the coffee shop, I took the lead to go over the things on our list to talk about. We tried to leave with decisions made or plans made on all the things on our list.

Thoughts for Single Parents

These same principles can work for single parents. Keep a small notebook somewhere accessible to record issues as they come up. You will solve a situation in the moment but then you may want to take time to be more thorough. Have time marked on your calendar when you think about the state of your family. It probably would be helpful to get out of the house and with other adults.

Break out your notebook and sort your issues in order of importance. Bring your concerns before the Lord asking for his wisdom. Is there something you should do differently? Is there some advice you need to seek out? And then return to the family with your new decisions as well as any follow-up actions you need to take.

The Benefits

This regular coffee date had numerous benefits. It pulled my focus back into the family. It reminded me that I was a dad leading a family, not just a pastor. It pulled Sharon's focus off of the children and back on me. It reminded her she was a wife, not just a mom. And it sent a message to the children that Mom and Dad care for each other and are taking time for their relationship.

Over time, the frequency changed as the schedules changed, but the essence was there.

Does every couple need to follow this pattern? Obviously not. But many family shepherds would benefit from this routine. Just as church shepherds benefit from regular meetings, so family shepherds need to sit down and discuss how their sheep are doing.

Try it. I think you will be surprised at the benefit.

APPENDIX 4
A Parable of Two Kind Police Officers

There once was a boy and a girl who grew up in a small town. As these stories go, Jonathan and Amy fell in love with each other and were married. But along the way they discovered something else they had in common—both loved their little town and they loved serving it.

In particular, Jonathan and Amy both loved keeping the peace and safety by being police officers. And so this husband and wife became officers of the law. And the community loved them. Two of their own would be serving the town!

Problems Arise

However, Jonathan and Amy soon realized that one particular aspect of their job was especially challenging. They had to give out speeding tickets. What made this a challenge was that, since they grew up in this town, they were giving the tickets out to their friends and people they loved.

At first they would just give their friends a warning. But they discovered that they were giving lots of warnings. Their friends never seemed to change. Then Jonathan and Amy found their own hearts getting upset that they had to stop so many people. They would come home from work frustrated that their friends were not heeding their warnings—they just kept speeding!

An Old-Timer's Advice

What were they going to do? They felt like the joy was being sucked out of their job. Finally, they decided to have breakfast with Frank, the retired policeman who had served the city for many years. They would ask his advice.

After they explained the situation to him, Frank sympathized a little bit and then said, "The solution is fairly simple. The question is, 'Will you take my advice and be consistent with it?'"

"Yes!" they said. "Anything. We love our jobs and the people. We are desperate."

Frank continued:

First, you must believe in the laws. Run for city council so you can change the silly speed limits. Make sure all the speed limits are realistic and an expression of love. Also make sure the fines are real deterrents. A $20 ticket will probably not stop the behavior.

Second, every day get ready for work knowing that part of your job will be to give people you love speeding tickets. They will plead with you and tell you they don't have the money. You will feel torn in your heart. But if they are speeding, you must enforce the law. Remember, it is an act of love for their good. They don't realize how these laws will save their lives and the lives of others.

Third, give out your tickets with care and without anger. You can even sympathize with them: "Oh, Mrs. Jones, are you speeding through this area again? Didn't I just give you a ticket last week? Well, this time the fine has to be doubled. I hope that will help you remember next time. I am doing this because I care."

It was that simple? thought Jonathan and Amy. *That was it?*

Jonathan and Amy had believed they were loving their friends by not giving tickets. Now they saw that loving their friends meant they had to give their friends tickets.

A Young Couple's New Perspective

And that's what the couple did.

1. They served on the city council so that all the speed limit laws were for people's real safety. There were no speed traps. They wanted their friends to have the maximum freedom and still have a safe, orderly community. But they also upped several fine amounts to be more effective.

2. Every day as they got ready to go to work, they knew they would encounter their friends speeding. They also knew they would be tempted to let them off with a warning. But they knew from past experience that only a real consequence would change behavior.

3. In addition, because they went to work expecting their friends to speed, they found that they were less angry. They gave out tickets, not because they were angry, but with a little tinge of sadness.

Guess what happened to their little town? With better speed limits, better enforcement, and kinder policemen, the accidents in the town dropped dramatically. Jonathan and Amy found themselves better liked. The drivers knew they were breaking the law and deserved the consequence.

Jonathan and Amy were happier. Their friends (eventually) were happier. And the town was safer. All because of a change of perspective.

Parents of young children, go and do likewise.

APPENDIX 5

Should You Let the Sun Go Down on Your Anger?

Ephesians 4:26 reads, "In your anger do not sin. Do not let the sun go down on your anger." It is a foundational verse on handling anger. And I am convinced that for years I misapplied this verse to the detriment of my marriage.

What exactly does this verse mean? And how should it be applied in marriage?

For many years, early in our marriage, Sharon and I tried to apply that verse literally. We had the normal adjustments of newly married couples. In addition, both of us have intense personalities. As a result, we had numerous times of "intense fellowship." In fact, we probably had those times more than most couples.

Often a disagreement would carry on as the evening grew late. The more we tried to "resolve" our disagreement the further we were to resolution. We were trying to not go to bed in our anger. And it wasn't working.

The Unsettling Effects of Anger

Our basic impulse was in the right direction based on human nature. If a couple has a disagreement and the relationship is tense, it is easy to just go to bed. One party sleeps on the couch, or they coldly sleep with their backs to each other. The next morning the issue is not resolved. In our minds we are still arguing with the other person. We are rehashing the hurt and the argument over and over. With no attempt at resolution, conflicts can simmer for days. A cold (or hot!) anger has settled over the house.

Given this natural working of human nature, God's gracious command makes sense. He is saying: Keep short accounts and don't let issues go unresolved.

Resolve the Issue Before Bed?

As a result of this understanding, Sharon and I tried to resolve each issue before we went to bed. We were thinking of the verse as, "Do not let the sun go down on the anger that is in your relationship. Resolve it." But for anyone who has ever tried to think straight after 10 p.m., the results were not helpful.

I am now convinced that our practice, while sincere, was based on a faulty understanding of this verse.

A more wise application would be to understand this verse in a different manner. Now I would argue that I do not need to resolve the issue that we were fighting about before bed. However, I do need to resolve my own anger.

Resolving the issue and the subsequent sinful words takes two people and may or may not happen. Letting go of my anger in forgiveness involves one person – me.

Resolve the Anger Before Bed

When applied this way, it is a command for me to control the only piece of real estate I can control – my heart. It is a command to acknowledge the disagreement and the anger and ask the Lord to resolve it.

Now I have a command to move from sinful anger to unconditional love. It is a chance for me to pray for good for a person I am at odds with at the moment. It is a chance for me to acknowledge to the Lord how much I feel hurt by this person and then pray, "Father forgive them." It is a chance for me to ask the Lord to show me the log in my own eye (Matt 7:3-5). It is a chance to pray that I would glorify God through this conflict (1 Cor 10:31). It is a chance to grow in unconditional love. I can pray, "Help me forgive as you have forgiven me. Help me pursue this one I disagree with the unconditional love you have shown me." And as we have seen in Lesson 3, it is a chance to spur me to action to resolve the issue at the appropriate time.

What this means is that, no, you do not have to resolve the issue you are arguing about that night. But it does mean you will resolve the upset before going to bed. You will sleep with a peaceful heart having entrusted the issue to the one who never sleeps. You can say something like, "This really upsets us right now, but I know we will figure it out. I love you. Let's set up a time when we have plenty of space for me to hear you out and you to hear me out."

Conclusion

Not going to sleep on your anger is a wise command from a loving Father. It may mean you resolve the issue before you go to bed. Or it may mean you wait until another time to talk about it when both are fresh. But what it does mean is that you don't go to bed with a heart full of anger. Your sleep is immersed in your own repentance, confession, unconditional love, and forgiveness. And that is a good way to fall asleep.

APPENDIX 6
The Character Chart

Parenting little (and big) children can feel like paddling down the rapids of a river in a raft. And then the raft turns over, and the family is being swept along by the current of activities chosen or imposed.

In Appendix 3, *The Power of the Coffee Date*, I have argued that a regular time away allows the shepherds of the family to think about the issues they are facing and come up with plans to address those. In this essay, I want to add another piece that helped us as a family – the Character Chart. I highlight it in my material – *Parenting with Confidence*.

The Character Chart is a written document that records the issues your family is working on. In the calm of the coffee date, the shepherds can decide what the most important issues are and what they will do about them.

The Columns

As you can see, it contains the following components:

Who – With four children running around, we needed this column to remind us and the children who this line applied to.

What to Put Off – What is the negative behavior we are trying to work on?

Consequence – What will be the negative consequence for this behavior? This is important for everyone to know the consequence. As a result, Mom and Dad can calmly give out the consequence (see Appendix 4, *A Parable of Two Kind Police Officers*). In addition, the children know beforehand what the result will be. They know Mom and Dad are not just making it up on the spot.

What to Put On – This is a vitally important column. The biblical pattern is to put off and put on. Sometimes our children don't know the positive we want them to aim for.

Scripture – Here we list a Scripture that can be quoted, memorized, or just referenced. We are showing that we are not just making this up, but we are acting under God's authority.

An Example of a Row

Who	What to put off	Consequence	What to put on	Scripture
R, C	Tattletaling	Chair for 3 minutes	"Mom, I think you ought to know about —"	Prov. 26:20, 22
K, C	Delayed Chore Obedience	Extra Chore	Immediate obedience	Col 3:20
R, N	Complaining about others	4 Thankful things	Thankfulness for your siblings	Col 3:17

The Reason It Works

The Character Chart works for several reasons.

1. It causes YOU to think – As you realize there are issues with your young children, the temptation can be to quickly assign a consequence or ignore the misbehavior. You don't think of it as character opportunity with a deliberate strategy. By filling out a form, you are forced to think and be deliberate.

2. It is written out for all to see – By putting it out for all to see, a husband and wife can be on the same page. In addition, the children know what you are working on. The consequence is right there in black and white. The positive quality is right there also.

3. It reminds you of the consequence – In the heat of the moment, it can be easy to forget the consequence. As a father who was in and out of the home, I found I usually needed reminding. At other times, a behavior disappears for a few days and then reappears. What was the consequence again? Check the chart.

4. It keeps you calm – Lastly, the chart keeps you calm. You don't have to get angry when you see the misbehavior. After all, you expected it. And you know what you will do. A simple process.

For additional information on how you can use the Character Chart to help shape the heart of your child, visit
www.theapollosproject.com/using-the-character-chart-to-shape-the-heart

Try it. I know it will be a blessing to your family. The next page has a blank character chart for you to copy and fill in.

Scripture	What to put on	Consequence	What to put off	Who

ENDNOTES

1. Robert D. Jones, *Uprooting Anger: Biblical Help for a Common Problem* (Phillipsburg, NJ: P&R Publishing, 2005), 15.

2. David Powlison, *Good and Angry: Redeeming Anger, Irritation, Complaining, and Bitterness* (Greensboro, NC: New Growth Press, 2016), 39.

3. Anger Journal credit to: David Powlison and Alasdair Groves, "Dynamics of Biblical Change," Christian Counseling & Educational Foundation, accessed August 1, 2019. https://www.ccef.org/course/dynamics-of-biblical-change/.

4. Jones, *Uprooting Anger*, 181.

5. Jay Adams, *The Christian Counselor's Manual* (Grand Rapids, MI: Zondervan, 1973), 360-361.

6. Dietrich Bonhoeffer, *Life Together: The Classic Exploration of Christian Community* (New York: HarperOne, 2009), 112-113.

7. Dietrich Bonhoeffer, *Life Together* (New York: Harper & Row, 1954), 112.

8. Powlison, *Good and Angry*, 1.

9. J.C. Ryle, *The Duties of Christian Parents to Their Children* (Sand Springs, OK: Grace and Truth Books, 2002), 19.

10. Chap Bettis, *The Disciple-Making Parent: A Comprehensive Guidebook for Raising Your Children to Love and Follow Jesus Christ* (Cumberland, RI: Diamond Hill Publishing, 2016), 65.

11. Based on a list in Jones, *Uprooting Anger*, 171-172.

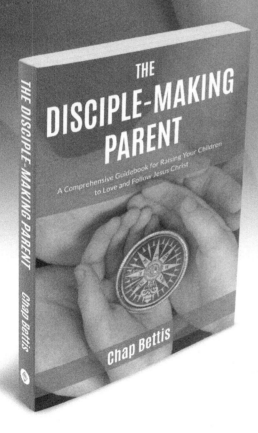

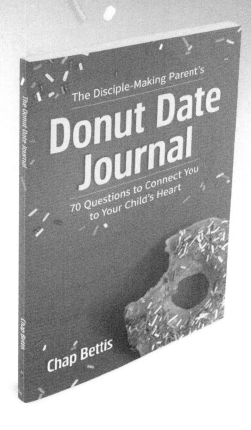

Made in the USA
Coppell, TX
22 December 2020